'MEMORY'

THE THEME FROM

Music by
ANDREW LLOYD WEBBER

Music © Copyright 1981 by The Really Useful Company Ltd
Text © Copyright 1981 by Trevor Nunn/Set Copyrights Ltd
First published in 1981 by Faber Music Ltd
3 Queen Square London WC1N 3AU
Mechanical and Publication Rights administered by Faber Music Ltd for the UK and Eire
Rights of dramatic performance administered by The Really Useful Company Ltd
Cover design ™ © Copyright 1981 by The Really Useful Company Ltd
Music processed by Jackie Leigh
Printed in England by Caligraving Ltd
All rights reserved

ISBN 0-571-50648-8

To buy Faber Music publications or to find out about the full range of titles available
please contact your local music retailer or Faber Music sales enquiries:

Faber Music Limited, Burnt Mill, Elizabeth Way, Harlow, CM20 2HX England
Tel: +44 (0)1279 82 89 82   Fax: +44 (0)1279 82 89 83
sales@fabermusic.com   fabermusic.com

FABER **ff** MUSIC

MEMORY

Text by TREVOR NUNN
after T.S. ELIOT

Music by
ANDREW LLOYD WEBBER

Albums from Faber Music

PIANO

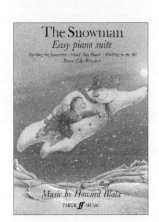

Cats (easy piano selection) *Andrew Lloyd Webber*

ISBN 0-571-50831-6

Children's Album *arranged by Daniel Scott*

ISBN 0-571-51103-1

The Faber Book of Showstoppers *arranged by Alan Gout*

ISBN 0-571-51063-9

The Faber Book of TV Themes *arranged by Alan Gout*

ISBN 0-571-51753-6

Great Film and TV Themes *Carl Davis*

ISBN 0-571-51740-4

Jane Austen's World *arranged by Richard Harris*

ISBN 0-571-51793-5

Shakespeare's World *arranged by Richard Harris*

ISBN 0-571-51907-5

The Snowman (easy piano suite) *Howard Blake*

ISBN 0-571-58044-0

FABER *ff* MUSIC

CAPTAIN CORELLI'S MANDOLIN

Music inspired by Louis de Bernières' novels
arranged for solo piano by Richard Harris

With a foreword by Louis de Bernières

ISBN 0-571-52092-8

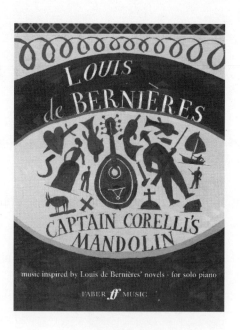

Captain Corelli's Mandolin has captured the hearts of readers all over the world; an extraordinary love story contrasting the brutality of war with the beauty of its Greek-island setting.

This collection brings together arrangements of music played by Captain Corelli himself and original pieces evoking the sounds and events of *Captain Corelli's Mandolin* and of three earlier novels—the Latin trilogy—by Louis de Bernières.

Alongside pieces inspired by the novels, little-known mandolin music is idiomatically arranged for piano by Richard Harris and contrasted with Neapolitan songs and folk songs from Latin America and Greece. Also featured is music by Stephen Warbeck, composer of the score for the film *Captain Corelli's Mandolin*.

"I might learn piano after all, and what might that lead to?"
Louis de Bernières

FABER *ff* MUSIC